V. Geyer

Raymond Briggs and Gail Ellis

The Snowman

The original storybook with activities for young learners of English

Additional illustrations by David Melling

Oxford University Press
1995

1   It's snowing!

1 What's James wearing?

Read and colour the picture.

James is wearing a red pullover, blue jeans, black boots, a red hat and red gloves.

James on a cold snowy day.

2 Winter clothes

Match the clothes to the colours and colour the clothes.

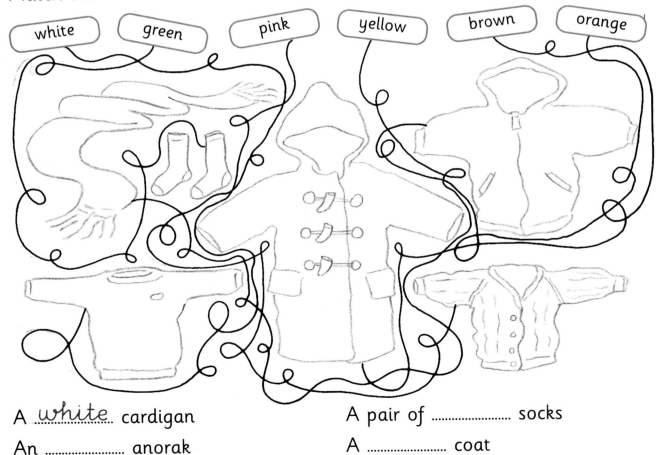

white   green   pink   yellow   brown   orange

A _white_ cardigan

An .... anorak

A .... scarf

A pair of .... socks

A .... coat

A .... sweatshirt

3 Draw and write.

I'm wearing ....

....

....

....

Me on a cold snowy day

4 Colours crossword

Write the colours in the boxes.

Across →   Down ↓

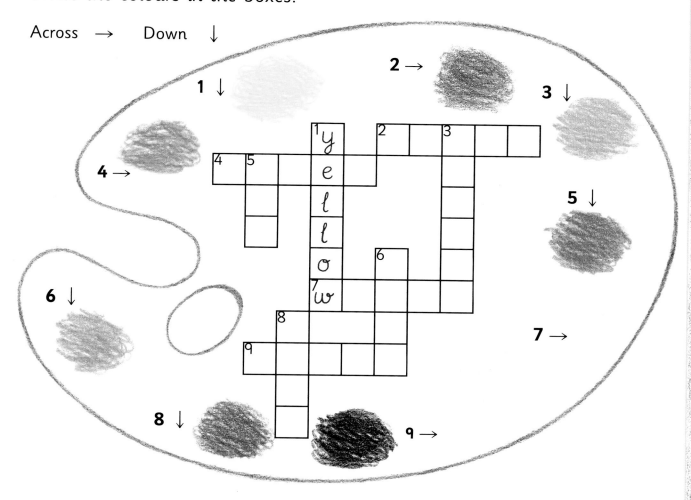

5 🎵 Sing the song on page 59.

This is the way I put on my pullover, ...

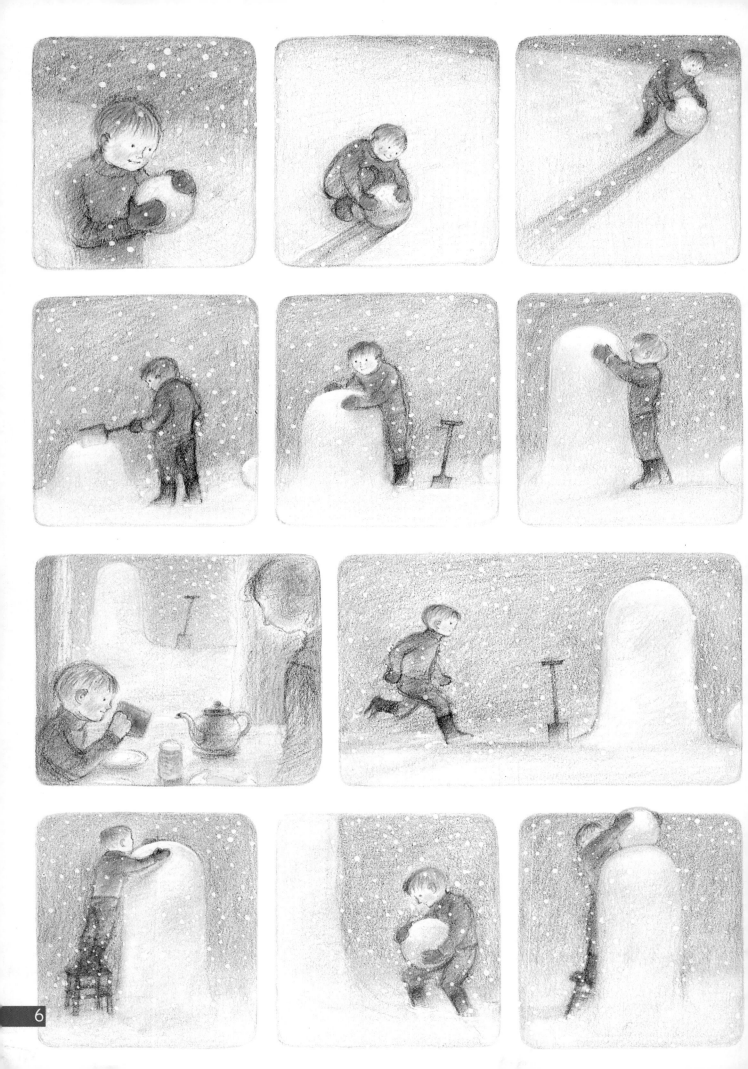

2 Building a snowman

1 Label the snowman.

Parts of the body

body
nose
head
mouth
arms
eyes
legs

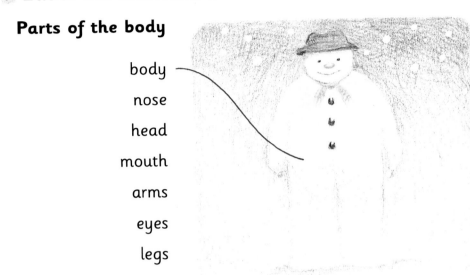

Clothes

scarf
hat
buttons

2 'What a wonderful snowman!'

Listen and number the pictures 1–8.

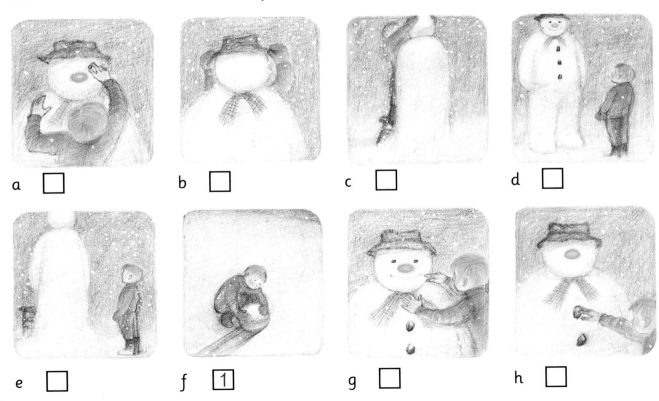

a ☐

b ☐

c ☐

d ☐

e ☐

f ☐ 1

g ☐

h ☐

3 Asking for permission

Can I ....
..................................?

Can I ....
..................................?

You ask.

Can I clean
the blackboard?

....

....

4 Game: Build a snowman.

5   Sing the song on page 59.

Head and shoulders, knees and toes ...

3 Going to bed

1 What's the time?

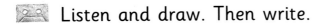 Listen and draw. Then write.

1 It's ....*two*.... o'clock.   2 It's .... o'clock.   3 It's .... o'clock.

4 It's .... eight.   5 It's .... o'clock.   6 It's ....

2 Time for bed!

Complete the sentences.

   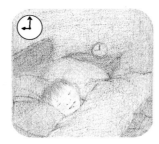      

1 James went to bed at *eight o'clock*

2 James fell asleep at ....

3 James woke up at ....

4 James crept downstairs at ....

3 What time do you go to bed?

Complete the questionnaire. Then ask
a friend.

	Questions	You	Your friend
	What time do you get up?		
	What time do you go to school?		
	What time do you have dinner?		
	What time do you go to bed?		

4 'How do you do!'

Match the greetings with the people.

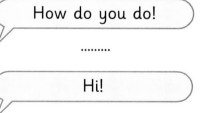

How do you do!

....

Hi!

....

Good morning!

...1....

Hello!

....

5   Say the rhyme on page 59.

Two fat snowmen ...

4 In the living room

1 Match the words with the furniture in
the living room.

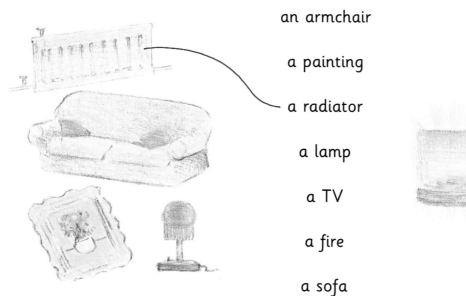

an armchair

a painting

a radiator

a lamp

a TV

a fire

a sofa

2 Find three things the Snowman likes
and three things he doesn't like.

B	D	Q	S	P	N	P	W	R
C	P	R	C	A	T	J	T	G
T	R	A	D	I	A	T	O	R
S	F	H	J	N	O	X	L	P
L	A	M	P	T	V	W	Z	Q
T	U	P	F	I	R	E	T	C
I	K	M	Q	N	R	X	B	Y
J	P	S	H	G	B	E	F	S

Now make sentences like this.

The Snowman likes the cat.   *The Snowman doesn't like the fire.*

16

3 'This is the living room.'

Here is a plan of James's living room. Draw a plan of your living room. Then show your friend around.

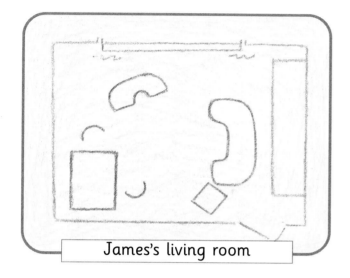

James's living room

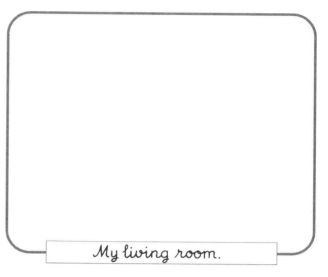

My living room.

4 Where's the Snowman?

between the chair and the sofa

behind the lamp

in front of the fire

Listen and draw the Snowman.

1

2

3

5 Game: Stand in front of the blackboard!

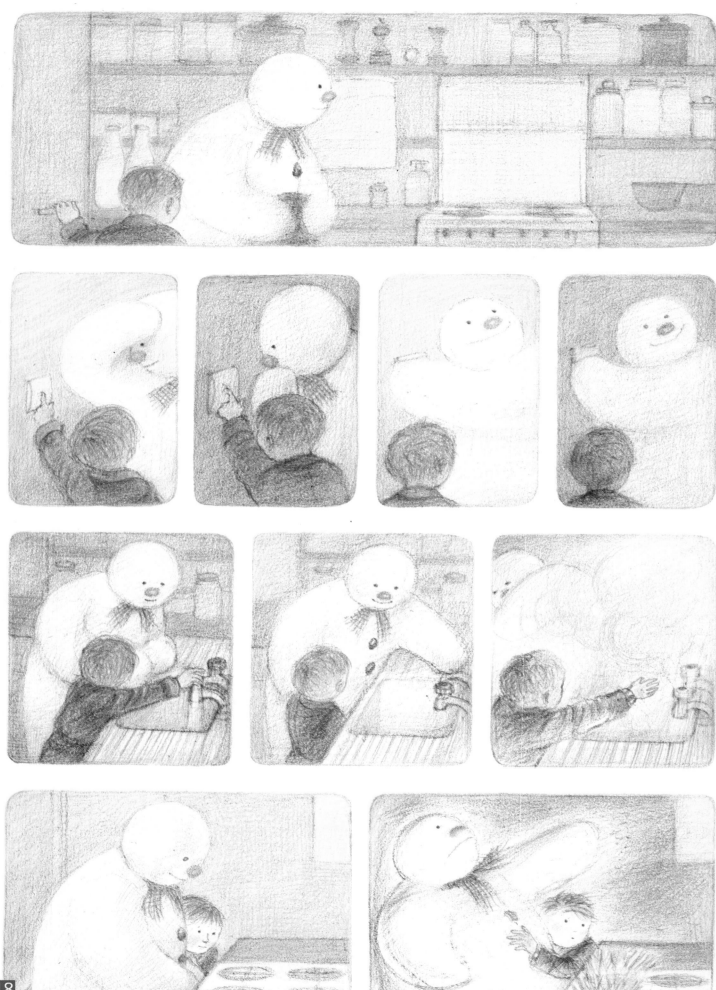

5 In the kitchen

1 Kitchen bingo

cooker	switch	tap	saucepan
washing-up liquid	salt and pepper	fridge	table
ice	sink	kitchen paper	jar

2 'This is the kitchen.'

Draw a plan of your kitchen. Then show your friend around.

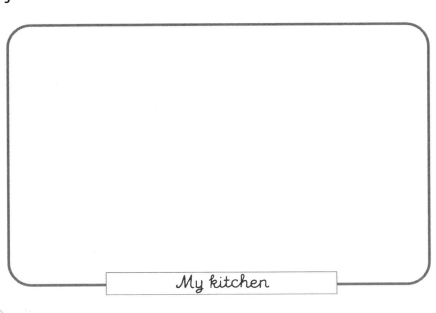

My kitchen

3 'Watch out!'

Match the warnings with the pictures.

1 |  2

3 | 4

Watch out! That's hot!

....

Watch out! That's sharp!

...1...

Watch out! That's dangerous!

....

Watch out! That's sticky!

....

4 Where's the saucepan?

on the table   under the table   in the sink

 Where's the ice? Listen and draw.

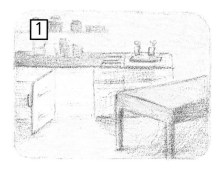 1 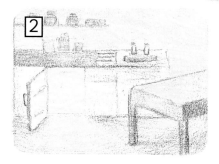 2  3

5 Say the chant.

A hot tap, a cold tap,
A cooker and a fridge.
Watch out, Snowman!
Hot things are bad.

21

6 My parents' bedroom

1 Match the words with the clothes.

a hat   trousers   glasses   a tie   braces

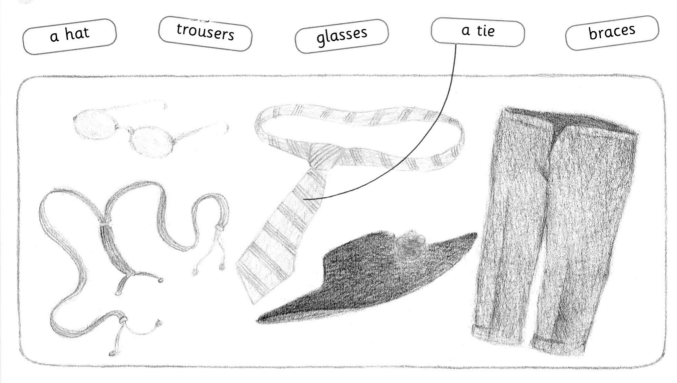

2 Listen, draw and colour.   3 Game: Dressing up!

Put on a hat!

Put on trousers!

4 'Let's go upstairs!'

Match the suggestions with the pictures.

Let's go downstairs!
....

Let's go outside!
....

Let's go in the kitchen!
....

Let's go in the bedroom!
...1....

5 Do the crossword.

Across

1

4

7

8

9

Down

1

2

3

4

5

6

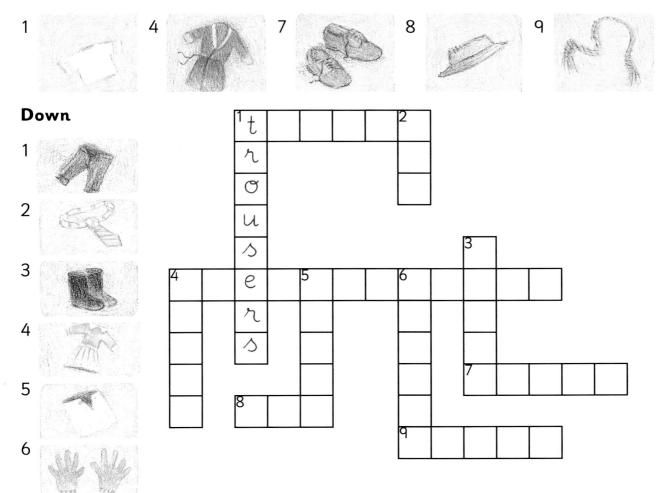

7 James's bedroom

1 Label the pictures.

skip · swim · skateboard · box · play the violin

1 skateboard ....

2 ....

3 ....

4 ....

5 ....

....

2 Can you skateboard?

James **can** skateboard.   The Snowman **can't** skateboard.

What about you?
I .... skateboard.
I .... swim.
I .... box.
I ....

Ask a friend. 'Can you skateboard?'
.... skateboard.
.... swim.
.... box.
....

3 🔊 Say the rhyme.

I can skip and I can swim,
But I can't play the violin.

4 How many balloons are there?

There are .... balloons.

Ask and answer.

1 There are

....

tangerines.

2 There are

....

lumps of coal.

3 There are

....

toothbrushes.

4 There are

....

ice cubes.

5 There are ....

saucepans.

5 Can you ...?

Can you name three winter clothes?   Yes ☐ No ☐ see page 4
Can you say what time James went to bed?   Yes ☐ No ☐ see page 12
Can you name three things the Snowman likes? Yes ☐ No ☐ see page 16
Can you name three rooms in James's house? Yes ☐ No ☐ see pages 16 and 20

8 The garage and the dining room

1   Listen and draw.

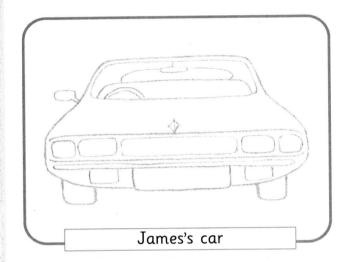

James's car

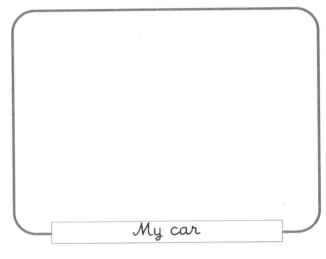

My car

2 What frozen food can you buy in your supermarket?

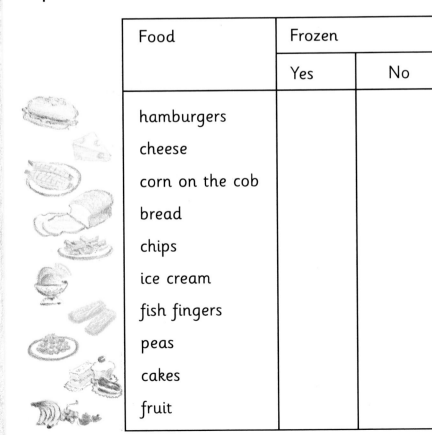

Food	Frozen	
	Yes	No
hamburgers		
cheese		
corn on the cob		
bread		
chips		
ice cream		
fish fingers		
peas		
cakes		
fruit		

Ask and answer.

Can you buy frozen bread?
Yes, you can.
No, you can't.

3 Write a midnight feast menu for a hungry snowman.

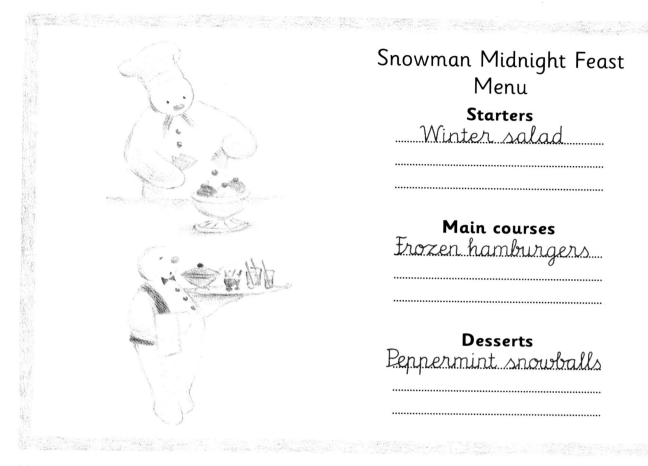

Snowman Midnight Feast Menu

Starters
...... *Winter salad* ......
....
....

Main courses
Frozen hamburgers .....
....
....

Desserts
Peppermint snowballs
....
....

You can make Peppermint Snowballs. Look at page 53.

4 Memory Game

Where did James and the Snowman go? Label the rooms in order.

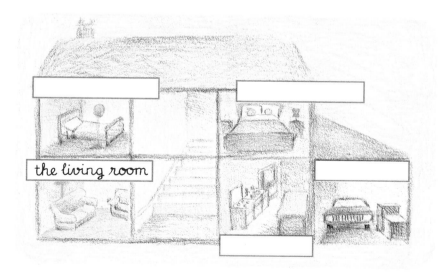

the living room

5 📼 **Rhyme.**

I like fish
But I don't like peas.
I like chips
But I don't like cheese.

9 Walking in the air

1 🎧 Listen and number the places you hear.

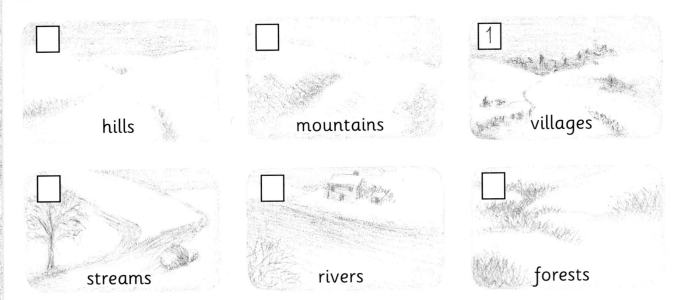

☐ hills   ☐ mountains   1 villages

☐ streams   ☐ rivers   ☐ forests

2 Across the snow.

across the snow   **through** the sky   **over** the town

Draw James and the Snowman.

through the tunnel   over the bridge   across the road

3 Colour the map.

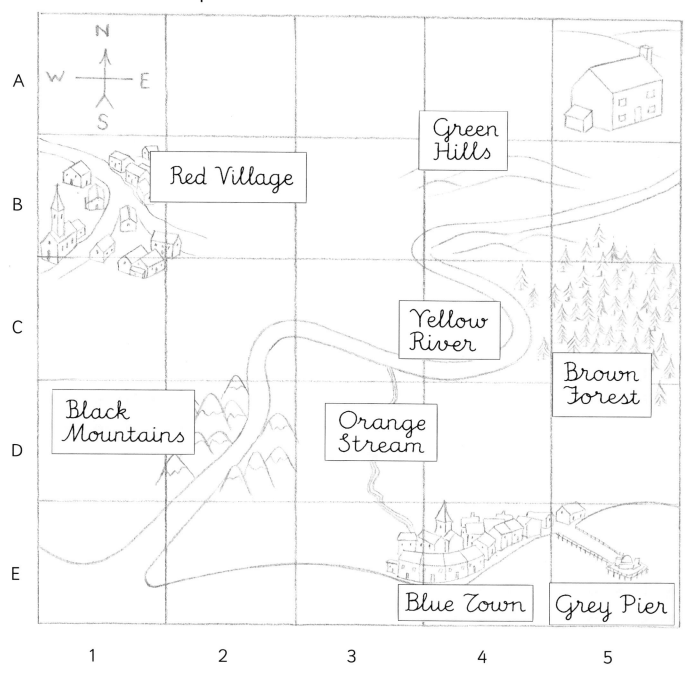

4 Look at the map

Where are these places?

James's house	5A
Red Village	
Green Hills	

What are these places?

5,C	Brown Forest
4,E	
2,D	

5 Listen and draw the Snowman's route on the map.

10 Back home

1 Listen and match the words with the pictures.

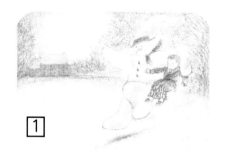 1

 2

 3

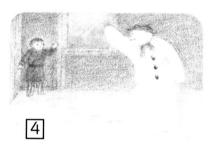 4

Goodnight.
Sleep well.
....

That was wonderful.
I've had a great time.
Thank you.
....

Goodbye! See you in
the morning.
....

Here we are back home.
...1...

2 What do you dream about?

		often	sometimes	never
	holidays			
	monsters			
	friends			

Make sentences like this.

I often dream about holidays.   I sometimes dream about monsters.

3 Sing the song on page 59.

There were five little snowmen ...

Make a snowflake

You need

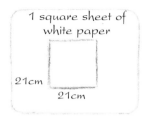
1 square sheet of white paper
21cm
21cm

scissors

a pencil

1 Fold here.

Open and fold here.
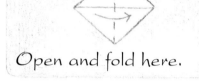

=
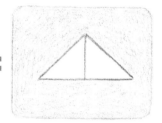

2 Fold here.
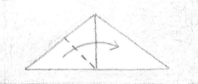

Now fold here.
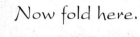
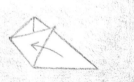

=
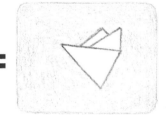

3 Turn over and draw a line here …

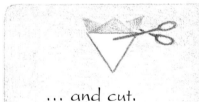
… and cut.

=
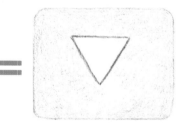

4 Open out …
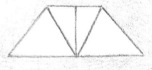

… and fold into pleats.
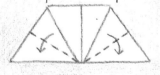

=
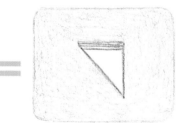

5 Draw a snowflake shape and cut out.

6 Open out your snowflake.

7 Now make your own snowflakes.

Peppermint Snowballs

You need

a sieve

two bowls

a whisk

a plate

scales

Recipe

230 grams of icing sugar

1 small egg white
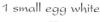

peppermint flavouring

1 Sieve the icing sugar into a bowl.

2 Whisk the egg white.

3 Add a few drops of peppermint flavouring.

4 Add to the icing sugar.

5 Knead until the mixture is stiff.

6 Roll into small balls and leave to harden.

Christmas around the world

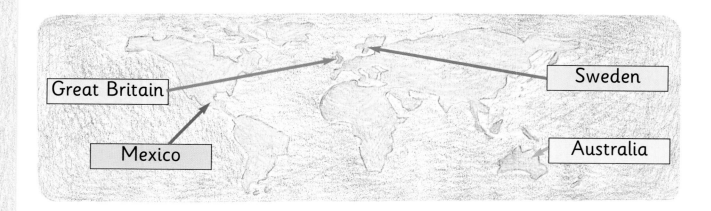

1 ....

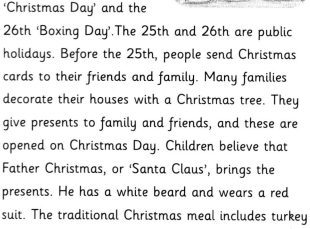

Christmas is the most important public holiday in the country. The 24th December is called 'Christmas Eve', the 25th 'Christmas Day' and the 26th 'Boxing Day'. The 25th and 26th are public holidays. Before the 25th, people send Christmas cards to their friends and family. Many families decorate their houses with a Christmas tree. They give presents to family and friends, and these are opened on Christmas Day. Children believe that Father Christmas, or 'Santa Claus', brings the presents. He has a white beard and wears a red suit. The traditional Christmas meal includes turkey and Christmas pudding. People pull crackers after the meal.

2 ....

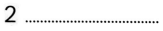

Christmas is celebrated for 9 days. On 16th December homes are decorated. This is the beginning of *Posadas* which recalls the story of the Holy Family's search for an inn. At family parties the *Piñata*, a decorated pottery jar filled with sweets and presents, is hung up. Blind-folded guests try to break it with a stick.

3 ....

The colours red and white are used for Christmas decorations. From the 1st December, beautiful stars and candles are put in windows. Christmas Eve is the most important day and the traditional meal includes dried cod and rice porridge.

4 ....

Christmas comes in the middle of the Summer. People give presents at breakfast and many people eat their Christmas Day meal on the beach. Homes are decorated with special flowers, like the 'Christmas bush', and with ferns and palm leaves. These are often decorated like a Christmas tree.

Make a Christmas card

You need

white card

scissors

coloured crayons

a black pen

1 Fold card.

2 Draw and cut out Snowman shape.

3 Write the greeting inside.

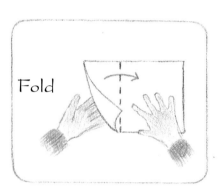
Fold

Make a Christmas cracker

You need

a cardboard tube

10 cm

coloured paper

ribbon

glue

scissors

a sweet

a joke
(see p. 56)

a paper hat

1 Put the paper hat, the sweet and the joke in the cardboard tube.
2 Roll the paper around the cardboard tube.
3 Glue the edges together.
4 Tie a piece of ribbon around each end.
5 Decorate your cracker.

Puzzles

1 Letter patterns

Write the **ice** letter pattern on each iceberg and match them to the pictures.

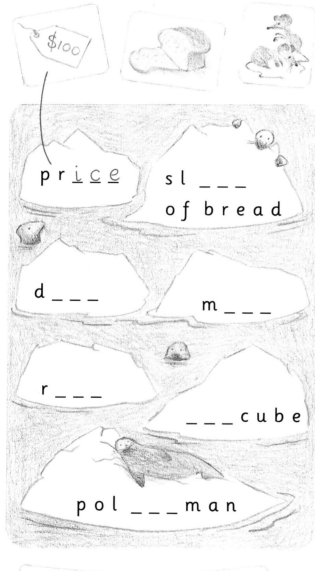

p r i c e

s l _ _ _
of bread

d _ _ _

m _ _ _

r _ _ _

_ _ _ c u b e

p o l _ _ _ m a n

2 Secret code

You can write in secret code.

5	A	B	C	D	E
4	F	G	H	I	J
3	K	L	M	N	O
2	P	Q/Z	R	S	T
1	U	V	W	X	Y
	1	2	3	4	5

S is in square (4,2)
N is in square (4,3)
O is in square (5,3)
W is in square (3,1)
So SNOW in code is
(4,2) (4,3) (5,3) (3,1)

Problem solving. What does this say?
(3,1) (3,4) (5,5) (3,2) (5,5)   (4,5) (5,3)
(4,2) (4,3) (5,3) (3,1) (3,3) (5,5) (4,3)
(4,5) (1,5) (4,3) (3,5) (5,5) ?

_ _ _ _ _   _ _
_ _ _ _ _ _ _   _ _ _ _ _ ?

(1,5) (5,2)   (5,2) (3,4) (5,5)
(4,2) (4,3) (5,3) (3,1)
(2,5) (1,5) (2,3) (2,3)

_ _   _ _ _   _ _ _ _ _ _ _ _

Write this joke on a piece of paper and put it in your cracker on page 55.

3 Do the Snowman crossword.

Across

2

4

6 It's white.

8

9

11

Down

1 It's black.

3

5

7

10

2. h a t

A day in the life of James

Write the times and match the sentences to the pictures.

1 James woke up at <u>eight o'clock</u> [e]

2 James started to build a snowman at .... ☐

3 James finished the snowman at .... ☐

4 James had tea at .... ☐

5 James went to bed at .... ☐

6 James crept downstairs at .... ☐

7 James and the Snowman flew up into the sky at .... ☐

8 James and the Snowman came back home at .... ☐

9 James woke up at .... ☐

a

b

c

d

e

f

g

h

i

Songs and rhymes

This is the way I put on my pullover *(page 5)*
This is the way I put on my pullover,
Put on my pullover, put on my pullover,
This is the way I put on my pullover,
On a cold and snowy morning.

This is the way I put on my jeans …

This is the way I put on my boots …

This is the way I put on my hat …

Head and shoulders, knees and toes … *(page 9)*
Head and shoulders, knees and toes,
Knees and toes,
Head and shoulders, knees and toes,
Knees and toes,
And eyes and ears and mouth and nose,
Head and shoulders, knees and toes,
Knees and toes.

Two fat snowmen *(page 13)*
Two fat snowmen met in a lane,
Bowed most politely, bowed once again,
How do you do,
How do you do,
And how do you do again?

Five little snowmen *(page 51)*
There were five little snowmen,
With scarves and woolly hats,
Out came the sun
And melted one.
It's sad –
But that was that!

There were four little snowmen, …

There were no little snowmen,
Just scarves and woolly hats,
Sitting in a puddle
In a very wet muddle;
It's sad –
But that is that!

A Christmas Carol
We wish you a merry Christmas,
We wish you a merry Christmas,
We wish you a merry Christmas,
And a happy New Year.
Good tidings we bring to you and your King.
We wish you a merry Christmas
And a happy New Year.

Walking in the air *words and music by Howard Blake* *(page 44)*
© Copyright 1982 by Highbridge Music Ltd. Publishing rights administered by Faber Music Ltd London. All rights reserved.

We're walking in the air
we're floating in the moonlit sky;
the people far below are sleeping as we fly.

I'm holding very tight,
I'm riding in the midnight blue,
I'm finding I can fly
so high above with you.

On across the world
the villages go by like dreams,
the rivers and the hills,
the forests and the streams.

Children gaze open-mouthed
taken by surprise;
nobody down below
believes their eyes.

We're surfing in the air,
we're swimming in the frozen sky,
we're drifting over icy mountains
floating by.

Suddenly, swooping low
on an ocean deep
rousing up a mighty monster
from his sleep.

We're walking in the air,
we're dancing in the midnight sky
and everyone who sees us
greets us as we fly.

The Snowman

ONCE UPON A TIME THERE WAS A BOY CALLED
James. One cold, winter morning in December,
James woke up and looked out of the window.

'Great!' he shouted. 'It's snowing!'

He got dressed quickly. He put on his red pullover
and his blue jeans.

'Mum! Can I go outside, please?' he asked.

'Yes, James. But don't forget to put on your boots,' she said.

So James put on his black boots, his red hat and his red gloves
and ran outside into the cold, white snow.

James started to make a snowball. Then he had a brilliant idea.

'I know,' he said. 'I'll build a snowman!'

First he made a big body. That was hard work so he had a quick
cup of tea. Then he put the snowball onto the body to make the
snowman's head, and he shaped his arms.

'I know!' thought James. 'He needs a hat and a scarf … Mum!
Can I have a hat and a scarf for my snowman, please?'

He put them on the snowman, gave him a tangerine for a nose
and lumps of coal for his buttons and for his eyes. Finally, he drew
a line for his mouth.

'Finished!' said James. 'What a wonderful snowman!'

'Tea time!' called James's Mum.

James went inside and had some toast. He couldn't stop thinking
about the snowman. Soon it was time for bed. He brushed his teeth
and put on his pyjamas.

'Goodnight, James. Sleep well.'

'Goodnight, Mum.'

James fell asleep but he soon woke up and got out of bed to look
at the snowman. It was midnight. He could not go back to sleep.

He put on his dressing gown and slippers, crept downstairs and opened the door. He couldn't believe his eyes … the Snowman moved! He took off his hat. He was a very polite Snowman.

'How do you do!' said James.

The Snowman walked slowly up to James and shook his hand.

'I'm James,' said James. 'Please come in.'

The Snowman took off his hat and came into the house.

'Sh! We must be quiet,' explained James. 'I'll show you around. This is the living room.'

The Snowman looked around and smiled.

'This is Kitty the cat.'

The Snowman liked Kitty.

'Meeeeow!' The Snowman's hand was very cold!

'This is the fire,' explained James.

Oh dear! The fire was very hot.

'This is the TV. Look!'

The Snowman was surprised.

'And this is the lamp. On. Off.'

The Snowman tried. On. Off. He was fascinated by everything.

'This is the radiator,' said James. 'It's very hot.'

The Snowman didn't like the radiator. He didn't like the painting either.

'This way,' said James.

'This is the kitchen,' said James, 'and this is a light switch. On. Off.'

The Snowman tried. On. Off.

'This is the sink, and this is the cold water tap,' explained James.

The Snowman turned on the other tap.

'Watch out! That's hot water,' warned James. 'This is the cooker.'

The Snowman turned on the gas.

'Watch out! That's hot!' warned James.

The Snowman picked up a plastic bottle and squeezed it.

Whoops! James laughed.

'That's washing-up liquid,' explained James.

The Snowman liked the kitchen paper.

'Stop!' said James. 'Look! Ice ...' It was delicious.

'And this is the fridge.'

The Snowman liked the fridge. It was lovely and cold.

'Sh! Let's go upstairs. This is my parents' bedroom. Mum and Dad are sleeping.'

The Snowman found a glass. But what were these?

'They're false teeth,' said James. 'Oh no! That's a photo of me!'

The Snowman dressed up. He put on a tie, glasses, trousers and braces and a big hat, and admired himself in the mirror. That was fun!

'Come on!' said James.

'This way. This is my bedroom. Look! I can skateboard. Can you?' asked James.

The Snowman tried, but he fell down.

'No, you can't. Are you all right? Come on, get up. Look! I can box. Can you?'

The Snowman tried again.

'Whoops! No, you can't. Oh dear! ... Look. This is a torch.'

The Snowman loved the torch. And what lovely balloons! Wheeee!

'Come on. Let's go downstairs,' said James. 'This is the garage and this is my parents' car. Let's go for a drive.'

They got in and the Snowman sat behind the steering wheel. Brrrr. Brrrr. Brrrrrm. Peep. Peep.

The Snowman turned on the headlights. Brrrr. Brrrr. Brrrrrm. That was a wonderful game.

They got out and James showed the Snowman the freezer.

'Look,' he said. 'It's freezing inside.'

The Snowman loved the freezer. He even got in and lay down.

He was very hot after the drive. Wonderful!

'Are you hungry?' asked James. 'Let's have a midnight feast.'

James took some packets of frozen food and they went into the dining room.

'Sit down,' said James, and he tied a napkin around the Snowman's neck.

'Here's your plate,' said James, and he served a delicious feast of frozen food.

They washed the dishes and then the Snowman took James by the hand.

They ran outside, across the snow and up, up into the air. They were walking in the air. They flew for miles through the cold moonlit sky over villages, rivers, hills, forests, streams and mountains.

Finally, they came to a town by the sea. They landed on a pier and looked at the sea.

Suddenly, the Snowman noticed the sun rising. It was time to go home. Up, up into the air they went again.

'Here we are back home,' said James.

The sun was beginning to shine. They walked towards the house.

'That was wonderful. I've had a great time. Thank you!'

James gave the Snowman a big hug.

'Goodnight. Sleep well,' said James. They waved goodbye.

'Goodbye. See you in the morning.'

James went upstairs and looked out of his bedroom window once more at the Snowman. Then, tired and happy, he fell asleep.

He woke suddenly to find the bright sunlight filling his room.

'The Snowman!' he cried. He put on his dressing gown and slippers and raced downstairs, without even saying 'Good morning' to his parents, and ran into the garden.

Where was the Snowman? Only a hat, a scarf and some lumps of coal lay on the ground …

Oxford University Press, Walton Street, Oxford OX2 6DP

Oxford   New York
Athens   Auckland   Bangkok   Bombay
Calcutta   Cape Town   China   Dar es Salaam
Delhi   Florence   Istanbul   Karachi
Kuala Lumpur   Madras   Madrid   Melbourne
Mexico City   Nairobi   Paris   Singapore
Taipei   Tokyo   Toronto
and associated companies in
Berlin   Ibadan

OXFORD and OXFORD ENGLISH
are trade marks of Oxford University Press

ISBN 0 19 422025 7

Original edition of THE SNOWMAN
copyright © 1978 Raymond Briggs
First published in Great Britain by Hamish Hamilton Ltd 1978

This adaptation of the original edition
© Oxford University Press 1995
The moral right of the author has been asserted.

The animated film, THE SNOWMAN, produced by SNOWMAN
ENTERPRISES LTD in 1982 is a TVC London production.

No unauthorized photocopying

All rights reserved. No part of this publication may be
reproduced, stored in a retrieval system, or transmitted,
in any form or by any means, electronic, mechanical,
photocopying, recording or otherwise, without the prior
written permission of Oxford University Press.

This book is sold subject to the condition that it shall not,
by way of trade or otherwise, be lent, re-sold, hired out,
or otherwise circulated without the publisher's prior consent
in any form of binding or cover other than that in which it
is published and without a similar condition including this
condition being imposed on the subsequent purchaser.

Printed in Spain